Verbal Reasoning

Rapid Tests 6

Siân Goodspeed

Schofield & Sims

Introduction

This book gives you practice in answering verbal reasoning questions quickly.

The questions are like the questions on the 11+ and other school selection tests. You must find the correct answers.

School selection tests are usually timed, so you need to get used to working quickly. Each test has a target time for you to work towards. You should time how long you spend on each test, or you can ask an adult to time you.

What you need

- A pencil
- An eraser
- A clock, watch or stopwatch
- A sheet of rough paper
- An adult to help you work out how long you take and to mark the test for you

What to do

- Turn to **Section 1 Test 1** on page 4. Look at the grey box at the top of the page labelled **Target time**. This tells you how long the test should take.
- When you are ready to start, write down the time or start the stopwatch. Or the adult helping you will tell you to begin.
- Find this black arrow ↓ near the top of the first page. Start each test here.
- Find this square ▪. The instructions for the first set of questions are beside it. Read them carefully.
- Look below the instructions. Read the **Example**. Work out why the answer given is correct.
- Use a similar method to answer question 1. Show your answer in the way that the answer is shown in the example. For instance, you might need to write your answer on the line or underline the correct answer from a selection given.
- Try to answer every question. If you do get stuck on a question, leave it and go on to the next one. Work quickly and try your best.
- Each test is one page long. When you reach the end, stop. Write down the time or stop the stopwatch. Or tell the adult that you have finished.
- With the adult, work out how long you took to do the test. Fill in the **Time taken** box at the end of the test.
- The adult will mark your test and fill in the **Score** and **Target met?** boxes.
- Turn to the **Progress chart** on page 40. Write your score in the box and colour in the graph to show how many questions you got right.
- Did you get some questions wrong? You should always have another go at them before you look at the answers. Then ask the adult to check your work and help you if you are still not sure.
- When you have finished working through this book, and are able to answer the questions both rapidly and correctly, you will be well prepared for school selection tests.

Published by **Schofield & Sims Ltd**,
Dogley Mill, Fenay Bridge, Huddersfield HD8 0NQ, UK
Telephone 01484 607080
www.schofieldandsims.co.uk
First published in 2014
This edition copyright © Schofield & Sims Ltd, 2018
Author: **Siân Goodspeed**. Siân Goodspeed has asserted her moral right under the Copyright, Designs and Patents Act, 1988, to be identified as the author of this work.
British Library Cataloguing in Publication Data. A catalogue record for this book is available from the British Library.

All rights reserved. No part of this publication may be reproduced, stored in a retrieval system, or transmitted in any form or by any means, electronic, mechanical, photocopying, recording or otherwise, without either the prior permission of the publisher or a licence permitting restricted copying in the United Kingdom issued by the Copyright Licensing Agency Limited, Saffron House, 6–10 Kirby Street, London EC1N 8TS.

Commissioned by **Carolyn Richardson Publishing Services** (www.publiserve.co.uk)
Design by **Oxford Designers & Illustrators**
Front cover design by **Ledgard Jepson Ltd**
Printed in the UK by **Page Bros (Norwich) Ltd**
ISBN 978 07217 1455 4

Contents

A **pull-out answers section** (pages A1 to A8) appears in the centre of this book, between pages 20 and 21. It also gives simple guidance on how best to use this book. Remove this section before the child begins working through the tests.

Target time: **10 minutes**

 Underline the two words, **one** from each group, that are most **similar** in meaning.

Example (<u>anger</u>, sadden, cross)   (<u>enrage</u>, grow, cry)

1. (reject, robust, yield)   (surrender, reluctant, roam)
2. (adversity, mystery, trickery)   (gravity, misfortune, symmetry)
3. (rotund, greedy, malicious)   (appeal, nutritious, avaricious)
4. (tranquillity, simplicity, audacity)   (improvement, indent, impudence)
5. (icon, acorn, eminent)   (bland, famous, signal)

In each of the sentences below, the word in capitals has three letters missing. Those three letters spell a word. Write the three-letter word on the line.

Example He was much **TER** than his younger brother.   <u>ALL</u>   (TALLER)

6. Their mum woke up the **EARST**. _____
7. She made several **ORS** in her spelling test.   _____
8. It was a long **JNEY** to get home.   _____
9. The girl felt really **MISBLE** when she heard the bad news.   _____
10. He always **EAVOURS** to finish his work on time.   _____

Find the missing number in each sequence and write it on the line.

Example 7   14   <u>21</u>   28   35   42   (+ 7 each time)

11. 24   12   6   3   _____   0.75   13. 2   4   6   10   16   _____
12. 145   220   295   370   445   _____   14. 16   25   36   _____   64   81

Work out the answers. Write your answers on the lines.

15. There are 15 pupils in a class. Of these children, 4 have blonde hair and 6 have brown hair. The number of children who have red hair is half the number of blondes, and the rest have black hair. How many children do not have red hair? _____

16. Daniel is inviting some people to his birthday party. He invites 7 friends from his class, 4 from his old school and 8 from his swimming club. The rest of the guests are his neighbours. There are a total of 25 people at his party, including him and his parents. How many people at the party are not from his class? _____

Score:		Time taken:		Target met?	

Target time: 10 minutes

Find the missing number in each of these equations and write it on the line.

Example 20 − 5 = 12 + ___3___

1. 79 + 2 = 9 × _____

2. 800 ÷ 100 = 2 × _____

3. 410 − 10 = 10 × _____

4. (56 × 10) + 50 = (70 × 9) − _____

5. 50 × 11 = (57 × 10) − _____

Underline the two words, **one** from each group, that are most **opposite** in meaning.

Example (friendly, <u>enemy</u>, silent)   (<u>ally</u>, kind, whisper)

6. (gaunt, sly, hollow)   (obese, cunning, gallant)

7. (eventual, frequency, frequent)   (celebratory, ocular, occasional)

8. (sum, estimate, divide)   (answer, calculate, circulate)

9. (questionable, important, quizzical)   (trivial, famed, powerful)

10. (transparent, trinket, optional)   (oblong, stampede, opaque)

Match the number codes to the words. One code is missing. Use this to help you work out the answers to the questions. Write your answers on the lines.

FIND   MEET   MIND   TIME   4182   6182   6779

What is the code for:

11. **FEET**? _____   12. **TIE**? _____   13. **DIME**? _____

14. What does the code **6187** mean? _____

Work out the answers. Write your answers on the lines.

15. Demi has a £10 note. She spends £7.79 on groceries and 85p on a bus ticket home. How much money does Demi have left? _____

16. Kris has 42 cupcakes. 12 are chocolate. There are twice as many vanilla cakes as there are chocolate. The rest of the cakes are lemon. How many lemon cakes does Kris have?

_____

Score:		Time taken:		Target met?	

Target time: **10 minutes**

Underline the two words, **one** from each group, that best complete the sentence.

Example Earth is to (mud, dirty, <u>planet</u>) as **cow** is to (field, <u>mammal</u>, bull).

1. **Joyful** is to (clown, elated, miserable) as **jealous** is to (envious, anxious, cross).

2. **Conclude** is to (terminate, commence, eliminate) as **pursue** is to (defy, chase, irritate).

3. **Understand** is to (listen, comprehend, instruction) as **delete** is to (omit, erase, undermine).

4. **Reasonable** is to (intellectual, persuasive, illogical) as **general** is to (specific, determine, select).

5. **Calculation** is to (computer, numeracy, exact) as **estimation** is to (imprecise, illegible, brain).

Use the information given to answer each sum. Write your answer as a **letter**.

Example A = 10   B = 6   C = 3   D = 12   E = 18   **B × C =** ___E___   (6 × 3 = 18)

6. A = 14   B = 36   C = 56   D = 9   E = 63   **C ÷ A × D =** _____

7. A = 4200   B = 12   C = 720   D = 640   E = 70   **A ÷ E × B =** _____

8. A = 2.3   B = 0.6   C = 3   D = 0.5   E = 1.9   **B × C + D =** _____

9. A = 3   B = 19   C = 35   D = 8   E = 45   **D² − B =** _____

10. A = 21   B = 42   C = 17   D = 207   E = 34 $\frac{E}{C}$ **× A =** _____

Find the missing letters in each sequence and write them on the line. Use the alphabet to help you.

A B C D E F G H I J K L M N O P Q R S T U V W X Y Z

Example Hi   Jk   Lm   No   ___Pq___   (first letter +2 capitals; second letter +2 lower case)

11. BX   FB   JF   _____

12. AH   YF   WD   _____   SZ

13. GC   DD   AE   _____   UG

14. KE   IG   _____   EK   CM

Work out the answers. Write your answers on the lines.

15. In 1 minute, Sasha takes 43 steps. It takes him 301 steps to travel from his house to the shops. If he leaves home at 10:24, at what time will he reach the shops if he walks steadily?

_____

16. Janine likes to sleep for 9 hours and 45 minutes every night. On Monday she needs to be awake at 7.25 a.m. What time should she go to bed on Sunday to get as much sleep as she would like?

_____

Score:		Time taken:		Target met?	

Schofield & Sims

Target time: 10 minutes

↓ Underline the pair of words that are most **opposite** in meaning.

Example (<u>lift, drop</u>) (snow, wind) (listen, learn)

1. (desperate, disparate) (intricate, detailed) (smart, slovenly)
2. (spendthrift, miser) (splinter, prison) (cell, master)
3. (around, about) (wax, wane) (during, while)
4. (heroic, infancy) (superior, inferior) (admiral, officer)
5. (material, fabric) (servile, servant) (automatic, manual)

Find **one** missing letter that completes **both** pairs of words. Write it on the lines.

Example strea [_m_] ile   doo [_m_] arry

6. elop [__] go   grap [__] very
7. acqui [__] alon   fein [__] wice
8. equi [__] arent   trum [__] earl

9. squea [__] arge   snar [__] urk
10. concer [__] ext   spou [__] rout

Using the alphabet to help you, find the letter pair that completes each sentence. Write it on the line. You might need to use a different method from the example given.

A B C D E F G H I J K L M N O P Q R S T U V W X Y Z

Example **FG** is to **EF** as **LM** is to ___KL___. (−1, −1)

11. **VE** is to **YA** as **KH** is to _____.
12. **DY** is to **XT** as **FJ** is to _____.
13. **JV** is to **QE** as **KU** is to _____.
14. **GR** is to **NP** as **IL** is to _____.

Circle the letter next to the **true** statement for each question.

15. Igneous rocks are formed when lava cools down. Basalt is an igneous rock.

If the above statements are true, which one of the following statements must also be true?
A Lava comes from volcanoes.
B Basalt is hot.
C Basalt can be ignited.
D Basalt is formed from cooled lava.

16. The Milky Way is a spiral galaxy. Saturn is a planet in the Milky Way.

If the above statements are true, which one of the following statements must also be true?
A Saturn is part of a spiral galaxy.
B Saturn has rings around it made of debris.
C Astronomers study spiral galaxies.
D Jupiter is next to Saturn.

Score:		Time taken:		Target met?	

↓

Find the **four-letter word** hidden across two or more consecutive words in each sentence below. The order of the letters must stay the same. Underline the word and write it on the line.

Example I like lots <u>of tr</u>eacle on my porridge! _____soft_____

1. My uncle favours chocolate cake over salad! _____

2. The drummer's cymbal makes an awfully loud noise. _____

3. I could not help him as I was myself on dangerous ground. _____

4. When I asked if you would like a gold medal I meant that you had won the race! _____

5. The wasp continued to hover beside the cake. _____

Underline the **two** words in each row that contain all the **same** letters.

Example <u>angel</u> gland ankle <u>glean</u> gleam

6. beaks baker bleak brave break   9. bores bloat robes broad boast

7. blare brain beard burnt bared   10. rules uncle clues cruel ulcer

8. being bring begin brain bench

Work out the missing numbers. Write them on the lines.

Example 11 [88] 8   9 [54] 6   15 [__45__] 3
($a \times b = ?$, where a represents the number on the left and b represents the number on the right)

11. 3 [26] 10   5 [20] 5   2 [_____] 2

12. 125 [150] 100   9 [10] 8   5 [_____] 1

13. 17 [64] 15   36 [72] 0   54 [_____] 6

14. 5 [34] 12   10 [88] 34   29 [_____] 11

Work out the answers. Write your answers on the lines.

15. I am going on holiday on 19 September. I will spend a day travelling to France. Then I will spend 2 days in France, after which I will spend a day travelling to Germany. I will spend 4 days in Germany, and then will spend 2 days travelling to England. On what date do I arrive in England? _____

16. It was my 11th birthday 248 days ago. If it is not a leap year, how many days is it until my next birthday? _____

Score:		Time taken:		Target met?	

Target time: 10 minutes

In each of the sentences below, the word in capitals has three letters missing. Those three letters spell a word. Write the three-letter word on the line.

Example He was much **TER** than his younger brother. _____ALL_____ (TALLER)

1. The vase was **PRLESS**. _____

2. The model broke because it was not very **ROT**. _____

3. The champion boxer remained **UNBEN**. _____

4. I opened the door to the **RESICE** of my aunt. _____

5. The naughty boy was punished **SRELY** by his mother. _____

Underline the two words, **one** from each group, that together make one new word. The word from the first group comes first.

Example (<u>tea</u>, coffee, cream)   (drink, <u>room</u>, milk)   (tearoom)

6. (night, dusk, sun)   (party, star, gown)

7. (old, new, brand)   (sprint, run, paper)

8. (lake, her, fish)   (ring, diamond, jewel)

9. (night, rodent, bat)   (he, us, person)

10. (hurt, scar, body)   (rush, let, buy)

Find the missing number in each of these equations and write it on the line.

Example $20 - 5 = 12 +$ ___3___

11. $(170 \div 10) \times 3 = 204 \div$ _____

12. $(70 + 50) \times 2 = 300 -$ _____

13. $10^2 + 12^2 = 245 -$ _____

14. $3^3 \times 5^2 = 200 + 150 +$ _____

Circle the letter next to the **true** statement for each question.

15. Meteorology is the study of the atmosphere. Cloud formations are part of the atmosphere.

If the above statements are true, which one of the following statements must also be true?
A Another name for rain is precipitation.
B Meteorologists study the formation of clouds.
C High pressure leads to warm weather.
D Clouds are always white or grey.

16. Creatures which can live in and out of water are called amphibians. Frogs live in and out of water.

If the above statements are true, which one of the following statements must also be true?
A Frogs are the same as toads.
B Frogs live beside ponds.
C Frogs eat flies.
D Frogs are amphibians.

Score:	Time taken:	Target met?

Target time: **10 minutes**

⬇ If these words were listed in alphabetical order, which word would come **third**? Write the answer on the line.

Example alert   ample   handle   hinder   ankle   _____ankle_____

1. harmonica   harmony   harp   harass   heaven   _____

2. leather   lethargy   liable   lentil   lethal   _____

3. wander   wonder   wondrous   window   wicked   _____

4. drab   dreary   derail   dread   drier   _____

5. caution   capsule   cautious   capital   capture   _____

In each group, three words go together and two are the odd ones out. Underline the **two** words that do **not** go with the other three.

Example <u>define</u>   certain   sure   <u>give</u>   definite

6. cymbal   bassoon   oboe   clarinet   cello

7. glockenspiel   harpsichord   piano   xylophone   chime bar

8. grotto   glade   cave   cavern   oasis

9. enrage   calm   placate   infuriate   exasperate

10. deform   renovate   refurbish   deface   disfigure

Underline the two words, **one** from each group, that together make one new word. The word from the first group comes first.

Example (<u>tea</u>, coffee, cream)   (drink, <u>room</u>, milk)   (tearoom)

11. (miss, left, right)   (out, take, over)   13. (building, out, over)   (site, light, burst)

12. (on, in, at)   (sign, risk, vest)   14. (sub, buck, rain)   (dew, doe, due)

Work out the answers. Write your answers on the lines.

15. There are 12 string instrument players and 14 brass instrument players in the school orchestra. Half the brass players play the trumpet and 3 of them play the horn. There are 2 drummers. How many people are there in the orchestra? _____

16. Nadya is organising a fashion show. Jamie, Alice, Susie and Li are modelling the outfits. Each wears 4 different outfits. All of Li's outfits are pink. Half of Alice's outfits are pink and the rest are red. One of Jamie's outfits is red; the others are blue. Susie wears 2 outfits with pink sequins on and the other 2 are plain white. How many outfits do **not** have pink on them?

_____

Score:		Time taken:		Target met?	

Target time: **10 minutes**

Underline the two words, **one** from each group, that are most **similar** in meaning.

Example (<u>anger</u>, sadden, cross)   (<u>enrage</u>, grow, cry)

1. (steel, steal, iron)   (platinum, crease, purloin)
2. (mandate, malady, hollow)   (masseur, illness, bellow)
3. (encircle, rectangular, shape)   (surround, dimension, square)
4. (precarious, graceful, physical)   (elongate, elaborate, elegant)
5. (courteous, illegible, ignorant)   (lawful, criminal, polite)

Change the first word into the last word. Only change **one** letter at a time, making two new four-letter words in the middle.

Example GILT [___SILT___] [___SALT___] MALT

6. RACE [_____] [_____] HIDE
7. TRIP [_____] [_____] PRAM
8. BOOK [_____] [_____] LOCH
9. TEND [_____] [_____] MEAL
10. SAND [_____] [_____] HINT

Using the alphabet to help you, crack the code. Write the answer on the line.

A B C D E F G H I J K L M N O P Q R S T U V W X Y Z

Example If the code for **SIT** is **TJU**, what is the code for **SAT**? ___TBU___

(+ 1 from the word to the code)

11. If the code for **HEADPHONES** is **IFBEQIPOFT**, what is **MUSICAL** in code? _____

12. If the code for **COATHANGER** is **EQCVJCPIGT**, what is **CURTAINS** in code? _____

13. If the code **RVFTUJPO** means **QUESTION**, what does the code **BOTXFS** mean? _____

14. If **EYELASH** is written in code as **ICIPEWL**, what is the code for **EYEBROW**? _____

Work out the answers. Write your answers on the lines.

15. Michelle is meeting her friend Melissa at 3.05 p.m. If she drove without stopping it would take her 34 minutes to travel to their meeting point. However, Michelle needs to stop for petrol on her way there. It will take her 5 minutes to fill her car with petrol and another 6 minutes to pay. What time should Michelle leave to be on time to meet Melissa? _____

16. How many minutes are there in 2.5 hours? _____

Score:		Time taken:		Target met?	

Target time: **10 minutes**

 Underline the word in the first group that goes best with the words in brackets.

Example <u>blue</u>, red, orange   (turquoise, navy, cyan)

1. postcard, telescope, vowel   (text, email, letter)
2. visit, hammer, measure   (anvil, mallet, saw)
3. tarragon, flagon, decagon   (octagon, hexagon, heptagon)
4. spend, blossom, spurn   (flourish, thrive, prosper)
5. saunter, sprint, row   (amble, stroll, meander)

Find the missing number in each of these equations and write it on the line.

Example $20 - 5 = 12 +$ ___3___

6. $130 \times 20 = 50^2 +$ _____
7. $40 + 30 - 75 = 15 -$ _____
8. $150 \times 50 = 10\,000 -$ _____
9. $20^2 + 20^3 = 4200 \times$ _____
10. $(15 \times 5) \div 2 = 35 +$ _____

Find the missing letters in each sequence and write them on the line. Use the alphabet to help you.

A B C D E F G H I J K L M N O P Q R S T U V W X Y Z

Example Hi Jk Lm No ___Pq___ (first letter +2 capitals; second letter +2 lower case)

11. BC   CD   DE   _____   FG
12. HH   HP   HX   HF   _____
13. PP   OQ   MS   JV   _____
14. ZP   PZ   GI   YQ   _____

Work out the answers. Write your answers on the lines.

15. There are 6 flavours of ice cream to choose from: chocolate, strawberry, mint, vanilla, hazelnut and orange. Betty orders 3 scoops of chocolate, mint and vanilla. Tam has the same as Betty with an extra scoop of orange. Kieran has orange and chocolate but is allergic to hazelnuts. Lucia orders all the flavours except mint. Which ice cream flavour do they **all** order?

_____

16. Selma and Imo are going to university. Between them they have 4 blue suitcases, 2 red suitcases and 3 brown suitcases. The brown suitcases are small; the rest are large. Each of their cars can hold 2 big suitcases and 1 small suitcase. How many cars do they need to fit in all their suitcases?

_____

Score: _____   **Time taken:** _____   **Target met?** _____

Schofield & Sims

Target time: 10 minutes

In each group, three words go together and two are the odd ones out. Underline the **two** words that do **not** go with the other three.

Example <u>define</u>   certain   sure   <u>give</u>   definite

1. lone   extrovert   solitary   single   social
2. consider   deliberate   assess   intend   mistake
3. convene   scatter   gather   disperse   assemble
4. polite   juice   cordial   rude   civil
5. ancient   abbreviate   archaic   brief   antique

In each of the sentences below, the word in capitals has three letters missing. Those three letters spell a word. Write the three-letter word on the line.

Example He was much **TER** than his younger brother.   _____ALL_____   (TALLER)

6. The hermit lived in **SOUDE**.   _____
7. The detective thought the fingerprints were a **SIGNIFIT** clue.   _____
8. The millionaire **SQUERED** his riches.   _____
9. The enemy **SURRERED** after a long battle.   _____
10. Our teacher put me and my friend in **SEATE** groups.   _____

Using the alphabet to help you, crack the code. Write the answer on the line.

A B C D E F G H I J K L M N O P Q R S T U V W X Y Z

Example If the code for **SIT** is **TJU**, what is the code for **SAT**?   _____TBU_____

(+ 1 from the word to the code)

11. If the code for **UMBRELLA** is **FNYIVOOZ**, what is **RAINFALL** in code?   _____
12. If the code **JCMNYPB** means **LEOPARD**, what does **RGECP** mean?   _____
13. If the code **NQZMFD** means **ORANGE**, what does **RBZQKDS** mean?   _____
14. If **GRASS** is written in code as **HRBST**, what is the code for **LAWN**?   _____

Use the word's definition to help you fill in the missing letters.

15. TH __ __ G __ TF __ __   considerate, pensive, attentive
16. AD __ __ N __ AG __   benefit, gain, "pro"

Score:		Time taken:		Target met?	

Target time: **10 minutes**

⬇ Move one letter from the first word to the second word to make two new words. Write the two new words on the lines.

Example trip, star _____rip_____ , _____start_____ (move the t)

1. ideal, beach _____ , _____

2. cable, lanes _____ , _____

3. pamper, other _____ , _____

4. brought, bawl _____ , _____

5. shingle, boot _____ , _____

Use the information given to answer each sum. Write your answer as a **letter**.

Example A = 10   B = 6   C = 3   D = 12   E = 18   **B × C =** ___E___ (6 × 3 = 18)

6. A = 9   B = 6   C = 12   D = 144   E = 2   **D ÷ E ÷ B =** _____

7. A = 9   B = −5   C = −8   D = 2   E = 12   **B + A − E =** _____

8. A = 120   B = 50   C = 108   D = 600   E = 115   **D ÷ B + C =** _____

9. A = 2   B = 1   C = 3   D = 4   E = 8 $\frac{B}{A} + \frac{A}{D} =$ _____

10. A = 37   B = 15   C = 5   D = 27   E = 9   **E × B ÷ C =** _____

The word in square brackets has been made by some of the letters from the two outside words. Make a new word in the middle of the second group of words in the same way. Write the new word on the line.

Example (help [hear] pair)   (soup [___sort___] grit)

11. (late [tail] list)   (lean [_____] warm)   13. (play [pile] live)   (mind [_____] lane)

12. (sign [sing] rain)   (reek [_____] loop)   14. (grain [bring] begin)   (rouse [_____] lords)

Work out the answers. Write your answers on the lines.

15. It takes Ling 45 minutes to do her homework and 50 minutes to do her chores. She wants to watch a television programme that starts at 7.15 p.m. What time must Ling start doing her homework and chores if she wants to be finished 5 minutes before her programme begins?
_____

16. Grace is 27. Her daughter is one-third of her age and her son is one-third of her daughter's age. How old is her son? _____

Score:		Time taken:		Target met?	

Schofield & Sims

Target time: **10 minutes**

Underline the word in brackets that is most **opposite** in meaning to the word in capitals.

Example LOUD   (noisy, <u>quiet</u>, shout, roar)

1. ANCESTOR   (dependent, traitor, descendant, dissent)
2. STATIONARY   (valuable, futile, mobile, pencil)
3. SHORTAGE   (surmise, surplus, lengthy, tallest)
4. AGGRESSIVE   (acquire, amiable, ferocious, angry)
5. ALTITUDE   (depth, mountainous, alternative, peak)

Find **one** missing letter that completes **both** pairs of words. Write it on the lines.

Example strea [_m_] ile   doo [_m_] arry

6. frot [__] angar   boot [__] aughty
7. cape [__] iddle   caree [__] evel
8. thrif [__] epid   flaun [__] alent

9. braw [__] avy   iro [__] iece
10. com [__] arley   tom [__] reach

Using the alphabet to help you, crack the code. Write the answer on the line.

A B C D E F G H I J K L M N O P Q R S T U V W X Y Z

Example If the code for **SIT** is **TJU**, what is the code for **SAT**?   _____TBU_____

(+ 1 from the word to the code)

11. If **ALPHABET** is written in code as **ZOKSZYVG**, what is the code for **EXAMINATION**?
_____

12. If the code **XSJOLMF** means **WRINKLE**, what does the code **NPJTUVSF** mean?
_____

13. If **SUNGLASSES** is written in code as **HFMTOZHHVH**, what is the code for **EXPRESSION**? _____

14. If the code for **STOPWATCH** is **TVRTBGAKQ**, what is the code for **TIMER**?
_____

Work out the answers. Write your answers on the lines.

15. There are 35 people on a bus. At the first bus stop, 12 people leave the bus and 5 get on. At the next stop, 11 people leave and 14 get on. How many people are now on the bus?
_____

16. Ali leaves for work at 8.20 a.m. It takes him 35 minutes to get to work. He has lunch 3 hours and 40 minutes later. What time does he have lunch? _____

Score:		Time taken:		Target met?	

Find the missing number in each sequence and write it on the line.

Example 7   14   __21__   28   35   42   (+ 7 each time)

1. 510   530   550   570   590   _____   **4.** 17   18   9   10   _____   6   3

2. 888   88.8   8.88   _____   0.0888   **5.** 56   28   14   7   _____

3. 16   32   64   128   _____   512

Underline the two words, **one** from each group, that together make one new word. The word from the first group comes first.

Example (<u>tea</u>, coffee, cream)   (drink, <u>room</u>, milk)   (tearoom)

6. (find, feed, cater)   (house, pillar, structure)   **9.** (family, aunt, relation)   (boat, ship, harbour)

7. (change, alter, new)   (native, own, equal)   **10.** (kit, bag, army)   (ten, twelve, organise)

8. (dirt, germ, cell)   (inate, proper, primal)

Match the number codes to the words. One code is missing. Use these to help you work out the answers to the questions. Write your answers on the lines.

TOMB   BOAT   COMB   MOAT   3487   7436   2436

What is the code for:

11. ATOM? _____   **12. TABOO**? _____   **13. COMMA**? _____
14. What does the code **34774** mean? _____

Circle the letter next to the **true** statement for each question.

15. Porcelain is a special type of clay used to make china objects. Gran's teapot is made from porcelain.

If the above statements are true, which one of the following statements must also be true?
A Clay is a type of china.   **C** Gran's teapot is made from special clay.
B Porcelain is expensive.   **D** Gran has china teacups.

16. Scandinavia is in the northern part of Europe. Scandinavia is formed of three countries: Norway, Denmark and Sweden.

If the above statements are true, which one of the following statements must also be true?
A Denmark is part of Scandinavia.   **C** It is always cold in Nordic countries.
B People who live in Scandinavia are called   **D** Iceland is a Nordic country.
   Norwegians.

Score: _____   Time taken: _____   Target met? _____

Target time: 10 minutes

↓ Underline the word in brackets that is **closest** in meaning to the word in capitals.

Example ERROR   (<u>mistake</u>, right, correct, answer)

1. DECEIVE   (decrease, cheat, dishevel, multiply)

2. CUNNING   (cautious, charming, sly, frustrating)

3. SINISTER   (silence, menacing, administer, welcoming)

4. VAST   (close, colossal, valley, mountain)

5. ABUNDANT   (plentiful, exacerbate, amplify, cruel)

Underline the two words, **one** from each group, that best complete the sentence.

Example **Earth** is to (mud, dirty, <u>planet</u>) as **cow** is to (field <u>mammal</u>, bull).

6. **Monday** is to (yesterday, Tuesday, Sunday) as **Friday** is to (Wednesday, tomorrow, Thursday).

7. **Feline** is to (tiger, chicken, hound) as **canine** is to (hyena, herbivore, cheetah).

8. **Esteem** is to (favour, disregard, admire) as **continue** is to (desist, resist, coexist).

9. **Exceptional** is to (allowable, pursuable, typical) as **ignorant** is to (educated, uncultured, neglected).

10. **Scarecrow** is to (farmer, birds, field) as **mannequin** is to (shop, surgery, clothes).

Find the missing letters or symbols in each sequence and write them on the line. Use the alphabet to help you.

A B C D E F G H I J K L M N O P Q R S T U V W X Y Z

Example Hi   Jk   Lm   No   __Pq__ (first letter +2 capitals; second letter +2 lower case)

11. BZ   GY   QX   FW   _____

12. Az   Cx   Gt   Mn   _____

13. AA   DE   BZ   JK   CY   PQ   _____

14. R%X   S*Z   U%B   X*D   _____

Work out the answers. Write your answers on the lines.

15. Stefan won the 100 metre sprint by 0.2 seconds. Finn was in second place, taking 17.75 seconds in total. How long did Stefan take? _____

16. Jon is baking biscuits for his brother's birthday party. It takes him 20 minutes' preparation time plus 12 minutes' baking time. He leaves the first batch in the oven for 15 minutes and they burn. He starts again with a new batch 5 minutes later. The biscuits are finally ready at 12.35 p.m. What time did he start making his first batch of biscuits? _____

Score:	Time taken:	Target met?

Target time: **10 minutes**

1–5. Look at the words in groups A, B, C and D. For each of the words below, choose the correct group and write its letter on the line.

A	B	C	D
nurse	solicitor	tutor	violinist

barrister _____   trainer _____   surgeon _____   judge _____   lecturer _____

headteacher _____   doctor _____   cellist _____   lawyer _____   flautist _____

Use the information given to answer each sum. Write your answer as a **letter**.

Example A = 10   B = 6   C = 3   D = 12   E = 18   **B × C =** ___E___   (6 × 3 = 18)

6. A = 98   B = 63   C = 271   D = 350   E = 4   **B × E + A =** _____

7. A = 0.9   B = 1.1   C = 0.8   D = 4   E = 1.6   **C ÷ D + A =** _____

8. A = 123   B = 75   C = 67   D = 115   E = 95   **C + A − B =** _____

9. A = 153   B = 81   C = 17   D = 146   E = 9   **B ÷ E × C =** _____

10. A = 16   B = 33   C = 7   D = 35   E = 21 $\frac{D}{C}$ **+ A =** _____

Using the alphabet to help you, find the letter pair that completes each sentence. Write it on the line. You might need to use a different method from the example given.

A B C D E F G H I J K L M N O P Q R S T U V W X Y Z

Example **FG** is to **EF** as **LM** is to ___KL___.   (−1, −1)

11. **SD** is to **HW** as **GY** is to _____.

13. **DW** is to **JA** as **VF** is to _____.

12. **MO** is to **ER** as **UF** is to _____.

14. **RA** is to **TV** as **HX** is to _____.

Work out the answers. Write your answers on the lines.

15. Annie, Sarah, Rav, Jason, Sydney and Louie belong to the school gymnastics team. Annie and Rav like doing somersaults and cartwheels and they are both able to use the balance bars. Louie hasn't learned how to do somersaults or back flips but he is really good at cartwheels. Louie and Sydney can use the balance bars but Sarah can't. Sydney and Sarah both like to do somersaults and back flips but Jason only does back flips. How many people can do back flips or somersaults? _____

16. Chloe competes in the Regional Swimming Championships. She swims the 200 metre race, alongside Jennie and Andrew. Then 6 different people swim the 50 metre race and 8 more people swim the 100 metre race. Finally, Cosima swims the 20 metre butterfly race with Michael, Cameron and Alexa. How many people swim races of 25 metres or longer? _____

Score: Time taken: Target met?

Target time: 10 minutes

In each group, three words go together and two are the odd ones out. Underline the **two** words that do **not** go with the other three.

Example <u>define</u>   certain   sure   <u>give</u>   definite

1. companion   enemy   foe   monarch   nemesis
2. pathetic   damp   pitiful   dismal   gloomy
3. danger   hazard   irritant   risk   scarce
4. grate   brilliant   dazzling   glazed   luminous
5. putrid   rotten   ridiculous   rancid   morbid

Underline the pair of words that are most **similar** in meaning.

Example (grow, shrink)   (age, young)   (<u>small, little</u>)

6. (dangle, suspend)   (aspect, general)   (elastic, string)
7. (average, implausible)   (amazement, wonder)   (release, attach)
8. (caring, affectionate)   (frosty, balmy)   (poignant, tactile)
9. (anticipate, eager)   (vile, exquisite)   (lethargic, languid)
10. (mature, infantile)   (bellow, under)   (recalcitrant, unruly)

Underline the two words, **one** from each group, that best complete the sentence.

Example Earth is to (mud, dirty, <u>planet</u>) as **cow** is to (field, <u>mammal</u>, bull).

11. **Robust** is to (fragile, tough, metallic) as **disgrace** is to (elegant, disrepute, grateful).
12. **Calm** is to (pacify, enrage, water) as **destroy** is to (disrepair, destruct, operate).
13. **Holiday** is to (pastime, leisure, family) as **workday** is to (pleasure, employ, business).
14. **Kindle** is to (book, camping, fire) as **brew** is to (potent, tea, vegetables).

Use the word's definition to help you fill in the missing letters.

15. T __ I __ M __ H   victory, accomplishment, achievement
16. QU __ __ Y   question, doubt, inquire

Score:		Time taken:		Target met?	

Target time: **10 minutes**

⬇ Work out the missing numbers. Write them on the lines.

Example 11 [88] 8   9 [54] 6   15 [___45___] 3
(a × b = ?, where a represents the number on the left and b represents the number on the right)

1. 13 [76] 25   55 [160] 25   23 [_____] 19   4. 42 [61] 23   11 [8] 14   25 [_____] 49

2. 7 [4] 10   25 [20] 30   44 [_____] 28   5. 20 [80] 20   5 [20] 5   10 [_____] 10

3. 21 [80] 19   70 [152] 6   29 [_____] 2

▨ Rearrange the word in capitals to make another word that goes with the first two. Write it on the line.

Example jump   skip   PALE   ___LEAP___

6. circle   square   HEAPS   _____   9. kind   mean   ULCER   _____

7. kidneys   lungs   EARTH   _____   10. noisy   loud   WORDY   _____

8. start   end   BEING   _____

▨ Underline **one** word from each set of brackets to complete the sentence best.

Example The (<u>dentist</u>, teacher, baby) told his patient that he would have to remove the decayed (dummy, book, <u>tooth</u>).

11. I sent out (books, newspapers, invitations) asking all my friends to my birthday (cake, party, house).

12. The (surgeon, fisherman, solicitor) performed a delicate (document, operation, element) on the (patient, visitor, boat).

13. The (celebrity, daughter, criminal) arrived at the (premiere, race, prison) in a (tank, limousine, moped).

14. My (manager, vicar, neighbour) informed me that I had been (envied, promoted, promised) to a more (minor, senior, fragile) position.

▨ Work out the answers. Write your answers on the lines.

15. Ben is racing his pet snails. Hotshot is in first place. Trailblazer is one place in front of Lickety, who is three places behind Whizzy. Slick is in third place, just behind Whizzy. Which snail is fourth to cross the finish line? _____

16. Eight people are taking part in a race. Bryony is coming third. Shelly is ahead of Emily and Ali but behind everybody else. Dev is two places ahead of Bryony. Damian is ahead of Simon but behind Bryony. Cindy is four places in front of Shelly. Who will cross the finish line in fourth position? _____

Score:	Time taken:	Target met?

Notes for parents, tutors, teachers and other adult helpers

- **Verbal Reasoning Rapid Tests 6** is designed for 11- and 12-year-olds, but may also be suitable for some older children.

- Remove this pull-out section before giving the book to the child.

- Before the child begins work on the first test, read together the instructions on page 2, headed **What to do**. As you do so, look together at **Section 1 Test 1** and point out to the child the different elements.

- As each question type is introduced for the first time within a particular test, an example is given. Where question types recur throughout the book, the same example is provided. This is deliberate: the example will act as a useful reminder, but children will not need to work through it repeatedly from scratch.

- Make sure that the child understands how to answer the questions and that he or she has a pencil, an eraser and a sheet of rough paper. You should also ensure that the child is able to see a clock or a watch.

- Explain to the child how he or she should go about timing the test. Alternatively, you may wish to time the test yourself. When the child has finished the test, you should together work out the **Time taken** and complete the box that appears at the end of the test.

- Mark the child's work using this pull-out section, giving one mark for each correct answer unless instructed otherwise. There are a total of 16 marks available for each test. Then complete the **Score** box at the end of the test.

- The table below shows you how to mark the **Target met?** box and the **Action** notes help you to plan the next step. However, these are suggestions only. Please use your own judgement as you decide how best to proceed.

Score	Time taken	Target met?	Action
1–8	Any	Not yet	Give the child the previous book in the series. Provide help and support as needed.
9–13	Any	Not yet	Encourage the child to keep practising using the tests in this book. The child may need to repeat some tests. If so, wait a few weeks, or the child may simply remember the correct answers. Provide help and support as needed.
14–16	Over target – child took too long	Not yet	
14–16	On target – child took suggested time or less	Yes	Encourage the child to keep practising using further tests in this book.

- After finishing each test, the child should fill in the **Progress chart** on page 40.

- Whatever the test score, always encourage the child to have another go at the questions that he or she got wrong – without looking at the solutions. If the child's answers are still incorrect, work through these questions together. Demonstrate the correct method if necessary.

- If the child struggles with particular question types, help him or her to develop the strategies needed.

Answers

Section 1 Test 1 (page 4)

1. yield, surrender
2. adversity, misfortune
3. greedy, avaricious
4. audacity, impudence
5. eminent, famous
6. LIE (EARLIEST)
7. ERR (ERRORS)
8. OUR (JOURNEY)
9. ERA (MISERABLE)
10. END (ENDEAVOURS)
11. 1.5 (÷2 each time)
12. 520 (+75 each time)
13. 26 (add previous two numbers)
14. 49 (square numbers)
15. 13
16. 17 (including Daniel as a person from his class)

Section 1 Test 2 (page 5)

1. 9
2. 4
3. 40
4. 20
5. 20
6. gaunt, obese
7. frequent, occasional
8. estimate, calculate
9. important, trivial
10. transparent, opaque
11. 4779
12. 917
13. 2167
14. MINE
15. £1.36
16. 6

Section 1 Test 3 (page 6)

1. elated, envious (synonyms)
2. terminate, chase (synonyms)
3. comprehend, erase (synonyms)
4. illogical, specific (antonyms)
5. exact, imprecise (calculations give exact answers whereas estimations are approximate)
6. B ([56 ÷ 14] × 9 = 36)
7. C ([4200 ÷ 70] × 12 = 720)
8. A ([0.6 × 3] + 0.5 = 2.3)
9. E ([8 × 8] − 19 = 45)
10. B ([34 ÷ 17] × 21 = 42)
11. NJ (+4, +4)
12. UB (−2, −2)
13. XF (−3, +1)
14. GI (−2, +2)
15. 10:31
16. 9.40 p.m./21:40

Section 1 Test 4 (page 7)

1. smart, slovenly
2. spendthrift, miser
3. wax, wane
4. superior, inferior
5. automatic, manual
6. e
7. t
8. p
9. l
10. t
11. ND (+3, −4)
12. ZE (−6, −5)
13. PF (mirror code)
14. PJ (+7, −2)
15. D
16. A

Section 1 Test 5 (page 8)

1. clef (My un<u>cle f</u>avours chocolate cake over salad!)
2. balm (The drummer's cy<u>mbal m</u>akes an awfully loud noise.)
3. fond (I could not help him as I was mysel<u>f on</u> dangerous ground.)
4. lime (When I asked if you would like a gold meda<u>l I</u> <u>me</u>ant that you had won the race!)
5. verb (The wasp continued to ho<u>ver be</u>side the cake.)
6. baker, break
7. beard, bared
8. being, begin
9. bores, robes
10. cruel, ulcer
11. 8 ([a + b] × 2)
12. 9 (2a − b)
13. 120 ([a + b] × 2)
14. 80 ([a + b] × 2)
15. 28 September
16. 117

Section 1 Test 6 (page 9)

1. ICE (PRICELESS)
2. BUS (ROBUST)
3. EAT or ATE (UNBEATEN)
4. DEN (RESIDENCE)
5. EVE (SEVERELY)
6. nightgown
7. newsprint
8. herring
9. bathe
10. scarlet
11. 4
12. 60
13. 1
14. 325
15. B
16. D

Section 1 Test 7 (page 10)

1. harmony
2. lethal
3. window
4. dread
5. capture
6. cymbal, cello (the others are wind instruments)
7. harpsichord, piano (the others are instruments that the player hits directly)
8. glade, oasis (the others are types of caves)

Schofield & Sims

9. calm, placate (the others are synonyms for irritate)
10. renovate, refurbish (the others mean to damage the appearance of something)
11. leftover
12. invest
13. outburst
14. subdue
15. 28
16. 8

Section 1 Test 8 (page 11)

1. steal, purloin
2. malady, illness
3. encircle, surround
4. graceful, elegant
5. courteous, polite
6. RACE [RICE] [RIDE] HIDE
7. TRIP [TRAP or TRIM] [TRAM or PRIM] PRAM
8. BOOK [LOOK] [LOCK] LOCH
9. TEND [MEND] [MEAD] MEAL
10. SAND [HAND] [HIND] HINT
11. NVTJDBM (+1 from word to code)
12. EWTVCKPU (+2 from word to code)
13. ANSWER (−1 from code to word)
14. ICIFVSA (+4 from word to code)
15. 2.20 p.m./14:20
16. 150

Section 1 Test 9 (page 12)

1. postcard (all forms of written communication)
2. hammer (all types of tools)
3. decagon (all 2D shapes)
4. blossom (all synonyms for flourish)

5. saunter (all ways of walking in a relaxed fashion)
6. 100
7. 20
8. 2500
9. 2
10. 2.5
11. EF (+1, +1)
12. HN (0, +8)
13. FZ (first letter −1, −2 etc.; second letter +1, +2, etc.)
14. RX (first letter −10, −9 etc.; second letter +10, +9, etc.)
15. chocolate
16. 3

Section 1 Test 10 (page 13)

1. extrovert, social (the others refer to being alone)
2. intend, mistake (the others are synonyms for consider)
3. scatter, disperse (the others are synonyms for gather)
4. juice, rude (the others are synonyms for polite)
5. abbreviate, brief (the others are synonyms for old)
6. LIT (SOLITUDE)
7. CAN (SIGNIFICANT)
8. AND (SQUANDERED)
9. END (SURRENDERED)
10. PAR (SEPARATE)
11. IZRMUZOO (mirror code)
12. TIGER (+2 from code to word)
13. SCARLET (+1 from code to word)
14. MAXN (+1, 0, +1, 0 from word to code)
15. THOUGHTFUL
16. ADVANTAGE

Section 1 Test 11 (page 14)

1. idea, bleach (move l)
2. able, lances (move c)
3. paper, mother (move m)
4. bought, brawl (move r)
5. single, booth (move h)
6. C ([144 ÷ 2] ÷ 6 = 12)
7. C (−5 + 9 − 12 = −8)
8. A ([600 ÷ 50] + 108 = 120)
9. B ($\frac{1}{2} + \frac{2}{4} = 1$)
10. D ([9 × 15] ÷ 5 = 27)
11. meal
12. rope
13. male
14. loser
15. 5.35 p.m./17:35
16. 3

Section 1 Test 12 (page 15)

1. descendant
2. mobile
3. surplus
4. amiable
5. depth
6. h
7. r
8. t
9. n
10. b
11. VCZNRMZGRLM (mirror code)
12. MOISTURE (−1 from code to word)
13. VCKIVHHRLM (mirror code)
14. UKPIW (+1, +2, +3, etc. from word to code)
15. 31
16. 12.35 p.m./12:35

Section 2 Test 1 (page 16)

1. 610 (+20)
2. 0.888 (÷10)
3. 256 (×2)
4. 5 (alternating +1 and ÷2)
5. 3.5 (÷2)

Answers

6. caterpillar
7. alternative
8. germinate
9. relationship
10. kitten
11. 8743
12. 78644
13. 24338
14. MOTTO
15. C
16. A

Section 2 Test 2
(page 17)

1. cheat
2. sly
3. menacing
4. colossal
5. plentiful
6. Sunday, Thursday (Sunday is the day before Monday and Thursday is the day before Friday.)
7. tiger, hyena (A tiger is a feline [cat] and a hyena is a canine [dog].)
8. disregard, desist (antonyms)
9. typical, educated (antonyms)
10. field, shop (You find a scarecrow in a field and a mannequin in a shop.)
11. ZV (+ multiples of 5, −1)
12. Uf (+ multiples of 2, − multiples of 2 and lower case letter)
13. DX (leapfrogging: +1, −1)
14. B%F (first letter +1, +2, etc.; second symbol alternating % *; third letter +2)
15. 17.55 seconds
16. 11.23 a.m./11:23

Section 2 Test 3
(page 18)

1–5. [score half a point for each correct answer]
A: surgeon, doctor (all jobs to do with medicine)
B: barrister, judge, lawyer (all jobs to do with the law)
C: trainer, lecturer, headteacher (all jobs to do with education)
D: cellist, flautist (all musicians)
6. D ([63 × 4] + 98 = 350)
7. B ([0.8 ÷ 4] + 0.9 = 1.1)
8. D ([67 + 123] − 75 = 115)
9. A ([81 ÷ 9] × 17 = 153)
10. E ([35 ÷ 7] + 16 = 21)
11. TB (mirror code)
12. MI (−8, +3)
13. BJ (+6, + 4)
14. JS (+2, −5)
15. 5 (everyone apart from Louie)
16. 17

Section 2 Test 4
(page 19)

1. companion, monarch (the others are synonyms for enemy)
2. pathetic, pitiful (the others refer to types of miserable weather)
3. irritant, scarce (the others are synonyms for danger)
4. grate, glazed (the others are synonyms for dazzling)
5. ridiculous, morbid (the others are synonyms for rotten)
6. dangle, suspend
7. amazement, wonder
8. caring, affectionate
9. lethargic, languid
10. recalcitrant, unruly
11. tough, disrepute (synonyms)
12. pacify, destruct (synonyms)
13. leisure, business (Holidays are leisure activities and workdays are business activities.)
14. fire, tea (Kindle is the precursor to fire and brew is the precursor to tea.)
15. TRIUMPH
16. QUERY

Section 2 Test 5
(page 20)

1. 84 ([a + b] × 2)
2. 60 (2a − b)
3. 62 ([a + b] × 2)
4. 1 (2a − b)
5. 40 ([a + b] × 2)
6. SHAPE
7. HEART
8. BEGIN
9. CRUEL
10. ROWDY
11. invitations, party
12. surgeon, operation, patient
13. celebrity, premiere, limousine
14. manager, promoted, senior
15. Trailblazer (order from first to last is Hotshot, Whizzy, Slick, Trailblazer, Lickety)
16. Damian (order from first to last is Dev, Cindy, Bryony, Damian, Simon, Shelly, Emily, Ali)

Section 2 Test 6
(page 21)

1. chaos
2. misery
3. disloyal
4. unknown
5. strong
6. insane
7. without
8. independent
9. message
10. director

Schofield & Sims

11. E (AAEE**E**GGRTX)
12. I (AAEE**I**LLTV)
13. H (ACCG**H**ILLOOPSY)
14. L (AAA**I**LMMMN)
15. Ruby (order from front to back of queue is Anna, Josh, Mel, Shameet, Ruby, Meg, Natalie)
16. Jana's (order of receiving food from first to last is Jeff, Gavin, Jana, Andy, Steve, Becky)

Section 2 Test 7 (page 22)

1. tact (Do no**t act** as if you know nothing about this!)
2. wren (We kno**w** **ren**egotiation is the only option.)
3. port (Do you want to sto**p or t**ry going on?)
4. owls (The lost wolf will h**owl s**o that it can find its pack.)
5. toad (Are you going t**o ad**dress the letter?)
6. rush, bland (move b)
7. tier, gash (move g)
8. cape, drone (move r)
9. order, bangle (move b)
10. imply, slaughter (move s)
11. c
12. f
13. k
14. t
15. first (order from tallest to shortest is Toby, Rachel, Jeremy, Zak and Monica, Beth)
16. paint (steps: 1. attach limbs; 2. put motor in; 3. paint; 4. wire in power button)

Section 2 Test 8 (page 23)

1. PONG [GONG] [GONE] GORE

2. LAID [LAND] [HAND] HANG
3. STOOL [STOOP] [STOMP] STAMP
4. DRINK [DRANK] [CRANK] CRANE
5. TRAIN [BRAIN] [BRAID] BRAND
6. ODE (ABODE)
7. SIT (ADVERSITY)
8. AMP (AMPLE)
9. FOR (UNFORTUNATE)
10. PAT (ANTICIPATED)
11. butterfly, delicate, perched
12. pleased, cousin, visiting
13. demolished, structure, unstable
14. schoolboy, belongings, satchel
15. Tuesday
16. 2

Section 2 Test 9 (page 24)

1. tamed
2. thank
3. grape
4. bloom
5. loose
6. mile, yard (the others describe timing in music)
7. manor, story (the others describe a person)
8. willing, gruelling (the others are synonyms for stubborn)
9. erase, emit (the others are synonyms for anchor)
10. report, history (the others are synonyms for myth)
11. 2.5 (÷2)
12. 2 (alternating ÷4, +2)
13. 184 (+56)
14. 1344 (×4)
15. 11.31 a.m./11:31
16. 8.40 a.m./8:40 in New York (1.40 p.m. UK time)

Section 2 Test 10 (page 25)

1. tyre (The par**ty re**mained noisy and crowded until midnight.)
2. gaze (Chasin**g a ze**bra makes good hunting practice for young lion cubs.)
3. exit (If you can read the ind**ex it**'s bound to be there.)
4. echo (Sh**e cho**se the pink coat to complement her green dress.)
5. sore (Birds may eat worm**s or e**ven slugs.)
6. stagecoach
7. airway
8. carrot
9. lifeline
10. thankless
11. clock (What time does the plane depart to Paris?)
12. they (My family and I live in a bungalow.)
13. his (She was delighted to pass all her exams.)
14. the (What is your favourite time of the year?)
15. 10/50 or 1/5 of the time (10 mins out of 50 mins)
16. 15 km/hour (There are 4 lots of 250 m in 1 km so it would take 4 minutes to travel 1 km and therefore 15 km in 1 hour.)

Section 2 Test 11 (page 26)

1. sender, planting (move l)
2. prove, pedal (move d)
3. light, flame (move f)
4. haven, ships (move s)
5. insect, pounce (move p)
6. 10
7. 100
8. 9

Answers

9. 7.5

10. 1.5

11. OkR (first letter +1; second letter −1 and lower case; third letter +1)

12. Vk (leapfrogging: first letter +1; second letter −1 lower case)

13. mM (first letter alternating i and m; second letter +1 each time)

14. YT (first letter −2; second letter +3)

15. 13 November (If 25 October is a Monday, 1 and 8 November are also Mondays; therefore the Saturday after Monday 8 will be 13 November.)

16. 4 Fridays (on 5, 12, 19, 26 August)

Section 2 Test 12
(page 27)

1. speech

2. bitter

3. bear

4. fire

5. mole

6. air helicopter (<u>Helicopters</u> are a form of <u>air</u> transport.)

7. Olympic ambition (My <u>ambition</u> is to be an <u>Olympic</u> gymnast.)

8. will weather (Whatever the <u>weather</u>, the match <u>will</u> go ahead.)

9. leap are (There <u>are</u> three hundred and sixty-six days in a <u>leap</u> year.)

10. of capital (Paris is the <u>capital</u> city <u>of</u> France.)

11. haven

12. reserved

13. distant

14. bigoted

15. £8.55 more

16. 9.38 a.m./09:38

Section 3 Test 1
(page 28)

1–5. *[score half a point for each correct answer]*
A: stubborn, wilful, inflexible (synonyms for obstinate)
B: retract, withdraw (synonyms for revoke)
C: timely, prompt (synonyms for punctual)
D: famous, well-known, important (synonyms for prominent)

6. wave (I sa<u>w a ve</u>ntriloquist at the theatre.)

7. soul (This route is shorter <u>so ul</u>timately we will get there sooner.)

8. nine (The carousel spu<u>n in</u> endless circles.)

9. slit (I gues<u>s lit</u>tle dogs are welcome in the hotel.)

10. dent (The ol<u>d ent</u>ertainers are usually the funniest.)

11. SOUL

12. GVOVKSLMV (mirror code)

13. WVORXRLFH (mirror code)

14. GREAT (position of letters in the alphabet where A=1, B=2, C=3, etc.)

15. ABSCOND

16. MANUSCRIPT

Section 3 Test 2
(page 29)

1. 12 ([a − b] × 2)

2. 28 (2a + b)

3. 75 (a ÷ [b ÷ 2])

4. 32 (a × 2b) or (2[a × b])

5. 29 (7a + b)

6. PETROL

7. MIRROR

8. COFFEE

9. WARMED

10. STORM

11. PAR (APPARITION)

12. TON (ASTONISHED)

13. CAT (CATASTROPHIC)

14. MEN (COMMENCE)

15. 8.55 a.m./08:55 (It takes him 20 minutes to travel 7 miles at 21 miles per hour.)

16. 2.5 km per hour

Section 3 Test 3
(page 30)

1. anything like (Goats <u>like</u> to eat <u>anything</u> they can find!)

2. enormous fisherman (The <u>fisherman</u> caught an <u>enormous</u> eel.)

3. afternoon strawberries (I like <u>strawberries</u> and cream for <u>afternoon</u> tea!)

4. for congratulated (The teacher <u>congratulated</u> her class <u>for</u> their hard work.)

5. millions roamed (Dinosaurs <u>roamed</u> the Earth <u>millions</u> of years ago.)

6. box

7. table

8. date

9. watch

10. crane

11. 3692

12. 8423

13. 986462

14. GNAW

15. Alex (order of arrival is Alex, Becki, Leo and Kate together, then Kara)

16. Poppy (order from left to right is Anne, James, Rishi, Max, Fran, Poppy)

Section 3 Test 4
(page 31)

1. mechanic

2. voluminous

3. knitted

4. course

5. obstruction

Schofield & Sims

6. KY (−3, −5)
7. ML (+8, −2)
8. EI (mirror code)
9. LS (+4, −5)
10. YX (−3, −2)
11. par
12. ten
13. con
14. ram
15. £13.80
16. 2/12 or 1/6

Section 3 Test 5 (page 32)

1. leek, soften (move s)
2. fume, drivel (move l)
3. moor, trust (move t)
4. arch, manger (move m)
5. left, chide (move c)
6. C ([750 + 250] − 550 = 450)
7. B ([549 ÷ 9] + 9 = 70)
8. B ([2 × 19] ÷ [14 ÷ 7] = 19)
9. B ([−10 − 4] + 17 = 3)
10. D ([310 − 34] ÷ 2 = 138)
11. SI (+5, −5)
12. YQ (first letter +8,+4,+2,+1; second letter +1,+2,+4,+8)
13. XC (first letter alternating +10, +5; second letter alternating +10, +5)
14. WR (W and X alternate, +1)
15. Lulu and Macey (order of the pairs from front to back is Lulu and Macey, Stella and Tim, Jack and Zhu, Melissa and Lewis, then Sam and Georgie)
16. Fred (order from front to back of the rope is Carys, Sara, Heather, Christopher, Fred, Angus, Marcus, Johnny)

Section 3 Test 6 (page 33)

1. B ([12 × 24] ÷ 2 = 144)

2. D ([100 − 65] ÷ 5 = 7)
3. A (7 × 14 × 0 = 0)
4. E ([25 − 45] + 36 = 16)
5. C ([3 × 55] ÷ 5 = 33)
6. TEAR
7. €∞©¡
8. ↑□□◊
9. RATS
10. VIEW (position of each letter in the alphabet plus 10: A=11, B=12, C=13, etc.)
11. instigate, initiate
12. sprightly, nimble
13. annual, yearly
14. mainstream, conventional
15. SURREAL
16. VINDICTIVE

Section 3 Test 7 (page 34)

1. pig
2. sun
3. pan
4. hand
5. horse
6. a
7. d
8. g
9. n
10. m
11. word (We will no<u>w order</u> dessert, please.)
12. reed (Take a spa<u>re ed</u>ition of the textbook from the professor's office.)
13. mast (My friend wants to ski<u>m a st</u>one across the lake.)
14. peak (Is a large a<u>pe a k</u>ind of monkey?)
15. 172 800 (60 secs × 60 mins × 48 hours)
16. 4 hours 14 mins 55 secs

Section 3 Test 8 (page 35)

1. 50 (a + b)
2. 53 (a + 2b)
3. 10 (4a − b)

4. 36 (5a + b)
5. 33 (3a + b)
6. immense, minute
7. liberty, captivity
8. help, hindrance
9. tranquil, agitated
10. obstinate, flexible
11. SLIP [SLAP or FLIP] [FLAP] FLAN
12. MILK [SILK] [SILT] SALT
13. GRAIN [BRAIN] [BRAWN] BRAWL
14. SLICE [SLIDE] [GLIDE] GLADE
15. C
16. B

Section 3 Test 9 (page 36)

1. misery (all types of emotions)
2. canyon (all land features that cut into the land)
3. toucan (all types of bird)
4. meteorite (all found in space)
5. thesaurus (all types of reference book)
6. upwards, sideways (synonyms)
7. valuable, inexpensive (Gold is worth a lot of money but tin is not.)
8. avoid, disgusting (synonyms)
9. fictitious, dissuade (antonyms)
10. infamous, uncover (synonyms)
11. lose
12. row
13. knit
14. beds
15. 25
16. 4.25 p.m./16:25

Answers

Section 3 Test 10 (page 37)

1. A ($[10 \times 10] + [2 \times 2 \times 2] = 108$)
2. C ($10 \times 6 \times 60 = 3600$)
3. B ($[27 \times 2] \div 6 = 9$)
4. D ($\frac{2}{4} - \frac{1}{2} = 0$)
5. A ($[99 \div 3] + 17 = 50$)
6. jumper, shirt (the others are types of material)
7. harmony, tranquillity (the others are synonyms for uproar)
8. exit, upstairs (the others are synonyms for captivate: note that 'entrance' has two possible meanings)
9. earth, ground (the others are all elements)
10. reckless, spiteful (the others are synonyms for kind)
11. ZJ (+7, +4)
12. CA (−6, +3)
13. SE (mirror code)
14. FG (+2, −6)
15. 38%
16. 44

Section 3 Test 11 (page 38)

1. understandable, operational (antonyms)
2. book, bookcase (Pages form a book and shelves form a bookcase.)
3. claim, abandon (synonyms)
4. standard, rotten (synonyms)
5. century, decade (There are 100 years in a century and 10 years in a decade.)
6. 34 (−9)
7. 64 (×2)
8. 9 (alternating)
9. 59 (alternating −1, +2)
10. 87 (+20)
11. t
12. o
13. y
14. l
15. 400 pages
16. 24

Section 3 Test 12 (page 39)

1. 50
2. 10
3. 10
4. 450
5. 30
6. accidental, intentional
7. summon, dismiss
8. luxury, squalor
9. fantasy, reality
10. incompetent, capable
11. 2996
12. 74969
13. 217796
14. SEEDS
15. C
16. B

This book of answers is a pull-out section from
Verbal Reasoning Rapid Tests 6

Published by **Schofield & Sims Ltd**,
Dogley Mill, Fenay Bridge, Huddersfield HD8 0NQ, UK
Telephone 01484 607080
www.schofieldandsims.co.uk
First published in 2014
This edition copyright © Schofield & Sims Ltd, 2018

Author: **Siân Goodspeed.** Siân Goodspeed has asserted her moral right under the Copyright, Designs and Patents Act, 1988, to be identified as the author of this work.

British Library Cataloguing in Publication Data. A catalogue record for this book is available from the British Library.

All rights reserved. No part of this publication may be reproduced, stored in a retrieval system, or transmitted in any form or by any means, electronic, mechanical, photocopying, recording or otherwise, without either the prior permission of the publisher or a licence permitting restricted copying in the United Kingdom issued by the Copyright Licensing Agency Limited, Saffron House, 6–10 Kirby Street, London EC1N 8TS.

Commissioned by **Carolyn Richardson Publishing Services** (www.publiserve.co.uk)

Design by **Oxford Designers & Illustrators**
Printed in the UK by **Page Bros (Norwich) Ltd**
ISBN 978 07217 1455 4

Schofield & Sims

Target time: **10 minutes**

Underline the word in brackets that is most **opposite** in meaning to the word in capitals.

Example LOUD   (noisy, <u>quiet</u>, shout, roar)

1. ORDER   (task, direct, chaos, assign)
2. JOY   (confusion, misery, jealousy, peace)
3. FAITHFUL   (disloyal, hopeful, reliable, honest)
4. RENOWNED   (forgiven, unknown, forlorn, famous)
5. WRETCHED   (sympathetic, stealthy, strong, weak)

Underline the two words, **one** from each group, that together make one new word. The word from the first group comes first.

Example (<u>tea</u>, coffee, cream)   (drink, <u>room</u>, milk)   (tearoom)

6. (in, around, outside)   (sane, safe, help)
7. (with, partner, friend)   (out, inn, room)
8. (inn, in, one)   (reliable, good, dependent)
9. (mess, state, tidy)   (old, age, young)
10. (straight, blunt, direct)   (either, or, any)

If the letters in the word were listed in alphabetical order, which letter would come **fifth**? Write the answer on the line.

Example DANCING   _I_   (ACDGINN)

11. EXAGGERATE   ____
12. ALLEVIATE   ____
13. PSYCHOLOGICAL   ____
14. MAMMALIAN   ____

Work out the answers. Write your answers on the lines.

15. Seven people are waiting for a bus. Ruby is three places behind Josh, who is standing in front of Mel. Anna is two places ahead of Mel. Natalie is two places behind Ruby who is in front of Meg. Shameet is standing in front of Ruby, right in the middle of the queue. Who will be the fifth person to get on the bus when it arrives? _____

16. Becky has gone to a restaurant with five friends and they are waiting for their food to be served. Becky's meal is last to arrive. Gavin's meal arrives before Jana's but after Jeff's. Jana's meal is served before Andy's. Steve's food arrives after Andy's. Whose meal is third to arrive? _____

Score:		Time taken:		Target met?	

Target time: **10 minutes**

Find the **four-letter word** hidden across two or more consecutive words in each sentence below. The order of the letters must stay the same. Underline the word and write it on the line.

Example I like lot<u>s of t</u>reacle on my porridge!   _____soft_____

1. Do not act as if you know nothing about this!   _____

2. We know renegotiation is the only option.   _____

3. Do you want to stop or try going on?   _____

4. The lost wolf will howl so that it can find its pack.   _____

5. Are you going to address the letter?   _____

Move one letter from the first word to the second word to make two new words. Write the two new words on the lines.

Example trip, star   _____rip_____ , _____start_____   (move the t)

6. brush, land   _____ , _____

7. tiger, ash   _____ , _____

8. caper, done   _____ , _____

9. border, angle   _____ , _____

10. simply, laughter   _____ , _____

Find **one** missing letter that completes **both** pairs of words. Write it on the lines.

Example strea [_m_] ile   doo [_m_] arry

11. tragi [__] omet   garli [__] ounter

12. aloo [__] lare   ree [__] ree

13. stor [__] ilo   dus [__] iln

14. clou [__] rawl   debu [__] high

Work out the answers. Write your answers on the lines.

15. Six people line up in height order from tallest to shortest. Jeremy is third from the front of the line. Beth is three places behind him. Rachel is not the tallest but she is taller than Zak and Monica. In what place in the line is Toby standing?   _____

16. Gita is following instructions to make a robot. There are four steps to follow. She is not supposed to paint the robot or put the motor in until after she has attached the arms and legs but, if she paints the robot before the motor is in, the robot will not work. The last thing to do is to wire in the power button. What is the third thing that Gita does to make the robot?

_____

Target time: **10 minutes**

Change the first word into the last word. Only change **one** letter at a time, making two new words in the middle.

Example GILT [_____SILT_____] [_____SALT_____] MALT

1. PONG [_____] [_____] GORE
2. LAID [_____] [_____] HANG
3. STOOL [_____] [_____] STAMP

4. DRINK [_____] [_____] CRANE
5. TRAIN [_____] [_____] BRAND

In each of the sentences below, the word in capitals has three letters missing. Those three letters spell a word. Write the three-letter word on the line.

Example He was much **TER** than his younger brother. _____ALL_____ (TALLER)

6. My **AB** was warm and homely. _____
7. She had overcome **ADVERY** to become successful. _____
8. His friend lent him **LE** money to buy a car. _____
9. The accident was **UNTUNATE**. _____
10. He **ANTICIED** that the weather would be fine for the picnic. _____

Underline **one** word from each set of brackets to complete the sentence best.

Example The (<u>dentist</u>, teacher, baby) told his patient that he would have to remove the decayed (dummy, book, <u>tooth</u>).

11. The (banjo, scorpion, butterfly) fluttered its (monochrome, delicate, repellent) wings as it (perched, stumbled, leant) upon a flower.
12. She was (pleased, distressed, annoyed) to hear that her favourite (canine, cousin, barrister) would be (evicting, trespassing, visiting) soon.
13. The building was (elevated, demolished, demonstrated) because its (paint, wallpaper, structure) was (unstable, forgotten, undamaged).
14. The (convict, schoolboy, fireman) carried his (cutlery, companion, belongings) in his (helmet, satchel, desktop).

Work out the answers. Write your answers on the lines.

15. If 8 February is a Friday, what day will 5 March be in a non-leap year? _____
16. How many fewer days are there altogether in November and September than in January and March? _____

Score:	Time taken:	Target met?

The word in square brackets has been made by some of the letters from the two outside words. Make a new word in the middle of the second group of words in the same way. Write the new word on the line.

Example (help [hear] pair)   (soup [___sort___] grit)

1. (later [learn] earned)   (three [_____] amidst)
2. (wizen [prize] proud)   (tanks [_____] think)
3. (spray [spare] reaps)   (grind [_____] pears)
4. (thirst [shirt] rushed)   (gloom [_____] sable)
5. (swing [twins] newts)   (goose [_____] stole)

In each group, three words go together and two are the odd ones out. Underline the **two** words that do **not** go with the other three.

Example <u>define</u>   certain   sure   <u>give</u>   definite

6. mile   tempo   beat   rhythm   yard
7. manner   demeanour   character   manor   story
8. willing   stubborn   inflexible   obstinate   gruelling
9. anchor   erase   cement   entrench   emit
10. report   myth   fable   history   legend

Find the missing number in each sequence and write it on the line.

Example 7   14   __21__   28   35   42   (+ 7 each time)

11. 80   40   20   10   5   _____   13. 16   72   128   _____   240
12. 88   22   24   6   8   _____   14. 21   84   336   _____   5376

Work out the answers. Write your answers on the lines.

15. Rinnie and Varma are meeting in the shopping mall at 11.30 a.m. Rinnie's watch is 10 minutes fast and when she arrives it shows the time as 11.35 a.m. Varma arrives 6 minutes after Rinnie. What is the real time when Varma arrives? _____

16. London is 5 hours ahead of New York. Stella leaves London at 6.35 a.m. UK time. The flight is usually 6 hours 45 minutes long but it is slowed down by turbulence and takes 20 minutes longer than usual. What will the time be in New York when Stella arrives? _____

Score:		Time taken:		Target met?	

Target time: **10 minutes**

Find the **four-letter word** hidden across two or more consecutive words in each sentence below. The order of the letters must stay the same. Underline the word and write it on the line.

Example I like lo<u>ts of t</u>reacle on my porridge! _____soft_____

1. The party remained noisy and crowded until midnight. _____
2. Chasing a zebra makes good hunting practice for young lion cubs. _____
3. If you can read the index it's bound to be in there. _____
4. She chose the pink coat to complement her green dress. _____
5. Birds may eat worms or even slugs. _____

Underline the two words, **one** from each group, that together make one new word. The word from the first group comes first.

Example (<u>tea</u>, coffee, cream)   (drink, <u>room</u>, milk)   (tearoom)

6. (theatre, stage, act)   (carriage, coach, teach)
7. (air, oxygen, breath)   (mask, plain, way)
8. (car, journey, vehicle)   (mould, rot, die)
9. (drop, life, jump)   (stick, line, straight)
10. (talk, thank, wist)   (less, you, full)

The words in the sentences below have been muddled up and an extra, unnecessary word has been added to each. Unjumble the sentences, then remove the extra word so that the sentences make sense. Cross out the extra word.

Example how you sandwiches would ~~much~~ many like   (How many sandwiches would you like?)

11. does time the clock plane what depart to Paris
12. bungalow and I live family in a they my
13. exams she was to pass delighted all her his
14. is what time the favourite of the year your

Work out the answers. Write your answers on the lines.

15. Terry takes 35 minutes to complete his maths exam paper. He then spends 5 minutes checking his answers and the rest of the time gazing out of the window. If the exam was meant to take 50 minutes, what proportion of that time did Terry spend gazing out of the window? _____

16. Mrs Moggins' hat blew away in a sudden gust of wind. It travelled for 250 metres before alighting on a tree 1 minute later. How fast was it travelling in km/hr? _____

Score:	Time taken:	Target met?

Target time: **10 minutes**

Move one letter from the first word to the second word to make two new words. Write the two new words on the lines.

Example trip, star _____rip_____ , _____start_____ (move the t)

1. slender, panting _____ , _____

2. proved, peal _____ , _____

3. flight, lame _____ , _____

4. shaven, hips _____ , _____

5. inspect, ounce _____ , _____

Find the missing number in each of these equations and write it on the line.

Example $20 - 5 = 12 +$ ___3___

6. $660 \div 6 = 11 \times$ _____

7. $110 \times 120 = 132 \times$ _____

8. $48 - 59 = -20 +$ _____

9. $325 \div 2 = 170 -$ _____

10. $6 (2.5 + 7.75) = 60 +$ _____

Find the missing letters in each sequence and write them on the line. You might need to use a different method from the example given. Use the alphabet to help you.

A B C D E F G H I J K L M N O P Q R S T U V W X Y Z

Example Hi Jk Lm No ___Pq___ (first letter +2 capitals; second letter +2 lower case)

11. LnO MmP NlQ _____ PjS QiT

12. Sn Xy Tm Za Ul Bc _____

13. iJ mK iL _____ iN mO

14. AQ _____ WW UZ SC QF

Work out the answers. Write your answers on the lines.

15. Jackson is organising a party for his mother's 70th birthday on 8 November. He is planning the party for the Saturday after her birthday. If it is Monday 25 October now, what will be the date of his mother's party? _____

16. How many Fridays will there be in August if 9 July is a Saturday? _____

Score:		Time taken:		Target met?	

Target time: **10 minutes**

From the five possible answers on the right, underline the word which goes equally well with both pairs of words in brackets.

Example (expensive, pricey)   (cherished, valued)   cheap   <u>dear</u>   precious   costly   loved

1. (talk, presentation)   (language, words)   voice   letter   speech   performance   audience
2. (freezing, chilly)   (sour, acidic)   winter   cold   ice   bitter   tart
3. (carry, support)   (tolerate, endure)   lift   accept   bear   withstand   hold
4. (shoot, discharge)   (flame, blaze)   fire   aim   explode   burn   gun
5. (spy, infiltrator)   (vole, rat)   agent   mole   detective   mouse   observe

Underline the **two** words in each sentence that need to change places in order for the sentence to make sense.

Example How do <u>your</u> like <u>you</u> tea?   (How do you like your tea?)

6. air are a form of helicopters transport
7. my Olympic is to be an ambition gymnast
8. whatever the will, the match weather go ahead

9. there leap three hundred and sixty-six days in a are year
10. Paris is the of city capital France

Underline the word in brackets that is **closest** in meaning to the word in capitals.

Example ERROR   (<u>mistake</u>, right, correct, answer)

11. SANCTUARY   (secret, haven, aquarium, desert)
12. RETICENT   (reserved, enthused, empowered, volatile)
13. REMOTE   (receive, likely, control, distant)
14. PREJUDICED   (just, bigoted, wise, proud)

Work out the answers. Write your answers on the lines.

15. Matthew earns £5.70 an hour on his paper round. His paper round normally takes him 2 hours, but today he has extra papers to deliver and it has taken him $3\frac{1}{2}$ hours. How much more has Matthew earned from today's paper round? _____

16. Mona arrived at the doctor's surgery at 9 a.m. She spoke to the receptionist for 4 minutes and then waited in the waiting room for 14 minutes. Her appointment lasted 13 minutes and then she walked home taking 7 minutes. What time did she get home? _____

Score:		Time taken:		Target met?	

1–5. Look at the words in groups A, B, C and D. For each of the words below, choose the correct group and write its letter on the line.

A	B	C	D
obstinate	revoke	punctual	prominent

timely _____   stubborn _____   famous _____   retract _____   well-known _____

prompt _____   withdraw _____   wilful _____   inflexible _____   important _____

Find the **four-letter word** hidden across two or more consecutive words in each sentence below. The order of the letters must stay the same. Underline the word and write it on the line.

Example I like lots <u>of t</u>reacle on my porridge!   _____ soft _____

6. I saw a ventriloquist at the theatre.   _____

7. This route is shorter so ultimately we will get there sooner.   _____

8. The carousel spun in endless circles.   _____

9. I guess little dogs are welcome in the hotel.   _____

10. The old entertainers are usually the funniest.   _____

Using the alphabet to help you, crack the code. Write the answer on the line.

A B C D E F G H I J K L M N O P Q R S T U V W X Y Z

Example If the code for **SIT** is **TJU**, what is the code for **SAT**?   _____ TBU _____

(+ 1 from the word to the code)

11. If the code for **LOUSE** is **$!*+5**, what does the code **+!*$** mean?   _____

12. If the code for **TOOTHACHE** is **GLLGSZXSV**, what is **TELEPHONE** in code?

_____

13. If the code for **CHOCOLATE** is **XSLXLOZGV**, what is **DELICIOUS** in code?

_____

14. If the code **4, 5, 1, 18** means **DEAR**, what does the code **7, 18, 5, 1, 20** mean?

_____

Use the word's definition to help you fill in the missing letters.

15. AB __ __ O __ D   escape, flee, desert

16. MA __ __ S __ RI __ T   music, document, text

Score: _____   Time taken: _____   Target met? _____

Target time: 10 minutes

↓ Work out the missing numbers. Write them on the lines.

Example 11 [88] 8   9 [54] 6   15 [_____45_____] 3
(a × b = ?, where a represents the number on the left and b represents the number on the right)

1. 44 [64] 12   56 [100] 6   24 [_____] 18
2. 28 [60] 4   10 [25] 5   12 [_____] 4
3. 86 [43] 4   24 [12] 4   150 [_____] 4

4. 9 [54] 3   4 [48] 6   8 [_____] 2
5. 2 [15] 1   3 [23] 2   4 [_____] 1

Rearrange the letters in capitals to make a new word so that the sentence makes sense. Write the new word on the line.

Example It was a dark and windy **GTHIN**.   __NIGHT__

6. The car ground to a halt because it had no **LOTPRE**. _____

7. The clown checked his makeup in the **RMRIRO**. _____

8. **FCFEEO** was the only thing that woke Mary up in the morning. _____

9. After a long rainy walk the dogs **DMRAEW** themselves by the fire. _____

10. The **MTSRO** rolled in over the hills making everything gloomy. _____

In each of the sentences below, the word in capitals has three letters missing. Those three letters spell a word. Write the three-letter word on the line.

Example He was much **TER** than his younger brother. _____ALL_____ (TALLER)

11. The ghostly **APITION** scared me. _____

12. The boy was **ASISHED** that he had won the prize. _____

13. The earthquake caused **ASTROPHIC** damage. _____

14. He waited for the lesson to **COMCE**. _____

Work out the answers. Write your answers on the lines.

15. Jaden travels to work on his bicycle at an average speed of 21 miles per hour. He needs to arrive in work at 9.15 a.m. in order to change and get ready for his start time of 9.30 a.m. If he lives 7 miles away from work, what time does he need to set out? _____

16. Izabell takes part in a sponsored walk. She takes 4 hours to walk the full distance of 10 km. What is her average speed? _____

Score:		Time taken:		Target met?	

↓ Underline the **two** words in each sentence that need to change places in order for the sentence to make sense.

Example How do <u>your</u> like <u>you</u> tea?   (How do you like your tea?)

1. goats anything to eat like they can find

2. the enormous caught an fisherman eel

3. I like afternoon and cream for strawberries tea

4. the teacher for her class congratulated their hard work

5. dinosaurs millions the Earth roamed of years ago

From the five possible answers on the right, underline the word which goes equally well with both pairs of words in brackets.

Example (expensive, pricey)   (cherished, valued) cheap <u>dear</u> precious costly loved

6. (fight, punch)   (container, cuboid)   hit box beat vessel cube

7. (counter, desk)   (chart, graph)   plot worktop diagram data table

8. (day, month)   (meeting, appointment)   year engagement date calendar conference

9. (clock, timepiece) (observe, see)   watch notice stopwatch witness timer

10. (hoist, winch)   (stork, flamingo)   lift pelican crane pulley crank

Match the number codes to the words. One code is missing. Use this to help you work out the answers to the questions. Write your answers on the lines.

SWING   GANG   AGAIN   SWAN   38462   92946   2962

What is the code for:

11. **SNAG**? _____   12. **WIGS**? _____   13. **AWNING**? _____

14. What does the code **2698** mean? _____

Work out the answers. Write your answers on the lines.

15. Becki and her friends are meeting up at a cafe. Alex arrives first and Kara arrives last. Leo and Kate arrive at the same time, just before Kara. Who does Becki arrive after?

_____

16. A class of students is posing for a school photograph. In the top row, are six students. Anne is on the far left, next to James. Between James and Poppy, there is Rishi, Max and Fran. Who is on the far right? _____

Score:		Time taken:		Target met?	

Target time: **10 minutes**

If these words were listed in **reverse alphabetical order**, which word would come **second**? Write the answer on the line.

Example improve   impress   empower   emperor   ample   ___impress___

1. mechanic   machine   mechanism   machinate   manoeuvre   _____
2. volume   volunteer   vocation   vacation   voluminous   _____
3. kinetic   knotted   knitted   kneaded   kinaesthetic   _____
4. colour   count   course   courgette   court   _____
5. obstacle   oblong   obese   obtuse   obstruction   _____

Using the alphabet to help you, find the letter pair that completes each sentence. Write it on the line. You might need to use a different method from the example given.

A B C D E F G H I J K L M N O P Q R S T U V W X Y Z

Example **FG** is to **EF** as **LM** is to ___KL___.   (−1, −1)

6. **BG** is to **YB** as **ND** is to _____.
7. **OT** is to **WR** as **EN** is to _____.
8. **XO** is to **CL** as **VR** is to _____.

9. **WD** is to **AY** as **HX** is to _____.
10. **PN** is to **ML** as **BZ** is to _____.

Each word below can be changed into a new word by putting another word in **front** of it. The added word should be the **same** for each word in the row. Find the added word and write it on the line.

Example buoy   line   boat   style   _____life_____

11. take   able   don   rot   _____
12. ant   don   fold   able   _____

13. course   tact   tent   descend   _____
14. pant   page   rod   shackle   _____

Work out the answers. Write your answers on the lines.

15. Marit has a budget of £20 for her charity bake sale. A pack of flour costs £2.20 and a packet of butter is £1.50. Marit also needs a pint of milk, at £1, and a pack of sugar. Two packs of sugar costs £3.00. How much change will Marit have once she has bought all her ingredients?

_____

16. Kim is choosing a kitten. There are 12 kittens in the litter, 4 of which are white. Half the litter are black and the rest are grey. What is the probability that Kim chooses a grey kitten?

_____

Score:		Time taken:		Target met?	

Target time: **10 minutes**

 Move one letter from the first word to the second word to make two new words. Write the two new words on the lines.

Example trip, star   _____rip_____ , _____start_____   (move the t)

1. sleek, often   _____ , _____

2. flume, drive   _____ , _____

3. motor, rust   _____ , _____

4. march, anger   _____ , _____

5. cleft, hide   _____ , _____

Use the information given to answer each sum. Write your answer as a **letter**.

Example A = 10   B = 6   C = 3   D = 12   E = 18   **B × C =** _____E_____   (6 × 3 = 18)

6. A = 550   B = 250   C = 450   D = 350   E = 750   **E + B − A =** _____

7. A = 9   B = 70   C = 549   D = 68   E = 79   **C ÷ A + A =** _____

8. A = 7   B = 19   C = 11   D = 14   E = 127   **2B ÷ (D ÷ A) =** _____

9. A = 17   B = 3   C = −10   D = −1   E = 4   **(C − E) + A =** _____

10. A = 155   B = 34   C = 310   D = 138   E = 2   **(C − B) ÷ E =** _____

Find the missing letters in each sequence and write them on the line. Use the alphabet to help you.

A B C D E F G H I J K L M N O P Q R S T U V W X Y Z

Example Hi   Jk   Lm   No   __Pq__   (first letter +2 capitals; second letter +2 lower case)

11. YC   DX   IS   NN   _____

12. JB   RC   VE   XI   _____

13. TY   DI   IN   SX   _____

14. WP   XQ   _____   XS   WT

Work out the answers. Write your answers on the lines.

15. Ten children are holding hands in a crocodile line. Sam and Georgie are at the back. Stella and Tim are in front of Jack and Zhu but behind Lulu and Macey. Melissa and Lewis are fourth in the line. Which pair are at the front? _____ and _____

16. Carys is part of her school tug-of-war team. She is at the front of the rope and Sara is behind her. Johnny is at the back with Marcus in front of him. Angus is in front of Marcus and Fred is in front of him. Christopher and Heather are between Fred and Sara, with the three girls behind one another. Who is fifth on the rope? _____

Score:	Time taken:	Target met?

Target time: **10 minutes**

↓

Use the information given to answer each sum. Write your answer as a **letter**.

Example A = 10   B = 6   C = 3   D = 12   E = 18   **B × C =** ___E___   (6 × 3 = 18)

1. A = 24   B = 144   C = 12   D = 132   E = 2   **C × A ÷ E =** _____

2. A = 5   B = 100   C = 65   D = 7   E = 77   **(B − C) ÷ A =** _____

3. A = 0   B = 14   C = 98   D = 7   E = 64   **D × B × A =** _____

4. A = 36   B = 45   C = 25   D = 27   E = 16   **(C − B) + A =** _____

5. A = 55   B = 5   C = 33   D = 21   E = 3   **E × A ÷ B =** _____

Using the alphabet to help you, crack the code. Write the answer on the line.

A B C D E F G H I J K L M N O P Q R S T U V W X Y Z

Example If the code for **SIT** is **TJU**, what is the code for **SAT**? ___TBU___

(+ 1 from the word to the code)

6. If the code ^&"£^ means **TREAT**, what does the code ^"£& mean? _____

7. If **DAZZLE** is written in code as €∞©©¤¡, what is the code for **DAZE**? _____

8. If the code for **ROOMY** is ◊□□↑Δ, what is the code for **MOOR**? _____

9. If the code for **STAR** is ∫ΣΠð, what does the code ðΠΣ∫ mean? _____

10. If **DRIVE** is written in code as **14**, **28**, **19**, **32**, **15**, what does the code **32**, **19**, **15**, **33** mean?

_____

Underline the pair of words that are most **similar** in meaning.

Example (grow, shrink)   (age, young)   (small, little)

11. (instigate, initiate)   (hope, pathos)   (allay, friend)

12. (enthuse, dampen)   (sprightly, nimble)   (resolute, courteous)

13. (annual, yearly)   (advent, calendar)   (egotistical, brave)

14. (excuse, blame)   (baron, peasant)   (mainstream, conventional)

Use the word's definition to help you fill in the missing letters.

15. SU __ __ E __ L   bizarre, strange, dreamlike

16. VI __ __ IC __ IV __   malicious, spiteful, mean

Score:	Time taken:	Target met?

Target time: **10 minutes**

Each word below can be changed into a new word by putting another word in **front**. The added word should be the **same** for each word in the row. Find the added word and write it on the line.

Example buoy   line   boat   style   _____life_____

1. tail   pen   eon   let   _____

2. dry   bathe   shine   burn   _____

3. try   cake   pipes   ache   _____

4. some   cuff   book   made   _____

5. play   hair   fly   radish   _____

Find **one** missing letter that completes **both** pairs of words. Write it on the lines.

Example strea [_m_] ile   doo [_m_] arry

6. cobr [__] brupt   quot [__] ward

7. shoul [__] rake   flui [__] rift

8. sprun [__] awk   strin [__] ale

9. shor [__] ape   spaw [__] otch

10. ato [__] irth   chas [__] arry

Find the **four-letter word** hidden across two or more consecutive words in each sentence below. The order of the letters must stay the same. Underline the word and write it on the line.

Example I like lots of treacle on my porridge!   _____soft_____

11. We will now order dessert, please.   _____

12. Take a spare edition of the textbook from the professor's office.   _____

13. My friend wants to skim a stone across the lake.   _____

14. Is a large ape a kind of monkey?   _____

Work out the answers. Write your answers on the lines.

15. How many seconds are there in 2 days?   _____

16. Miles beats his friend, Troy, in a marathon by 10 minutes 15 seconds. If Troy took 4 hours 25 minutes 10 seconds, how long did Miles take?   _____

Score:		Time taken:		Target met?	

Schofield & Sims

Target time: 10 minutes

Work out the missing numbers. Write them on the lines.

Example 11 [88] 8   9 [54] 6   15 [___45___] 3
(a × b = ?, where a represents the number on the left and b represents the number on the right)

1. 17 [20] 3   42 [50] 8   36 [_____] 14   **4.** 2 [17] 7   4 [23] 3   7 [_____] 1
2. 5 [35] 15   2 [98] 48   5 [_____] 24   **5.** 3 [10] 1   4 [15] 3   10 [_____] 3
3. 2 [3] 5   10 [25] 15   4 [_____] 6

Underline the two words, **one** from each group, that are most **opposite** in meaning.

Example (friendly, <u>enemy</u>, silent)   (<u>ally</u>, kind, whisper)

6. (brilliant, hour, immense)   (minute, detest, utilise)
7. (poisonous, liberty, popularity)   (captivity, capacity, secrecy)
8. (help, hesitate, holler)   (hexagon, hindrance, habit)
9. (entranced, transport, tranquil)   (adjust, agitated, turquoise)
10. (obstinate, obstacle, occupied)   (blockage, flexible, faded)

Change the first word into the last word. Only change **one** letter at a time, making two new words in the middle.

Example GILT [___SILT___] [___SALT___] MALT

11. SLIP [_____] [_____] FLAN   **13.** GRAIN [_____] [_____] BRAWL
12. MILK [_____] [_____] SALT   **14.** SLICE [_____] [_____] GLADE

Circle the letter next to the **true** statement for each question.

15. Nomadic people move from place to place to make a living. Bedouin tribes are nomadic.

If the above statements are true, which one of the following statements must also be true?
  A Bedouin people ride on camels.   **C** Bedouin people move from place to place.
  B Nomadic people live in tents.   **D** Tribes are always nomadic.

16. The study of stars, planets and galaxies is called astronomy. Mr Singh is an astronomer.

If the above statements are true, which one of the following statements must also be true?
  A Mr Singh writes horoscopes.   **C** Astronomers use telescopes.
  B Mr Singh studies stars, planets and galaxies.   **D** Astrologists build space rockets.

Score:	Time taken:	Target met?

⬇ Underline the word in the first group that goes best with the words in brackets.

Example <u>blue</u>, red, orange   (turquoise, navy, cyan)

1. misery, mentality, emotional   (jealousy, melancholy, ecstasy)
2. mountainous, canyon, peak   (crevasse, crevice, abyss)
3. lynx, toucan, trout   (heron, flamingo, pelican)
4. meteorite, meteorology, astronomer   (asteroid, meteor, satellite)
5. knowledge, thesaurus, synonym   (almanac, encyclopaedia, dictionary)

Underline the two words, **one** from each group, that best complete the sentence.

Example **Earth** is to (mud, dirty, <u>planet</u>) as **cow** is to (field, <u>mammal</u>, bull).

6. **Vertical** is to (upwards, axis, measured) as **horizontal** is to (degrees, sideways, downwards).
7. **Gold** is to (luminous, valuable, jewellery) as **tin** is to (inexpensive, unworthy, useless).
8. **Avert** is to (challenge, worship, avoid) as **grotesque** is to (disgusting, unimpressive, elegant).
9. **Factual** is to (documentary, pretentious, fictitious) as **persuade** is to (discuss, dissuade, disuse).
10. **Notorious** is to (infamous, remarkable, hazardous) as **expose** is to (situation, uncover, impose).

Make a new word by changing the first word of the third pair in the same way as the other pairs. Write the new word on the line.

Example lantern, ant   loneliest, one   marching, _____arc_____   (take the 2nd, 3rd, 4th letters)

11. striped, trip   cleaner, lean   closest, _____
12. tallow, low   window, now   marrow, _____
13. meals, slam   plots, stop   think, _____
14. fallow, fowl   turner, tern   bussed, _____

Work out the answers. Write your answers on the lines.

15. If the year 2000 was a leap year, how many leap years will there be altogether in the 21st century? _____

16. Zygus is on holiday in San Francisco. He catches the 8.55 a.m. tram from outside his hotel into the city centre. He alights 15 minutes later. Zygus then spends 3 hours sightseeing before going into a nearby restaurant where he has lunch for $1\frac{1}{2}$ hours. Following lunch, Zygus spends 2.5 hours shopping before catching another tram back to his hotel, 15 minutes away. What time does Zygus arrive back at his hotel? _____

Score:	Time taken:	Target met?

Target time: **10 minutes**

Use the information given to answer each sum. Write your answer as a **letter**.

Example A = 10   B = 6   C = 3   D = 12   E = 18   **B × C =** ___E___   (6 × 3 = 18)

1. A = 108   B = 96   C = 2   D = 10   E = 117   **D² + C³ =** _____

2. A = 60   B = 10   C = 3600   D = 6   E = 360   **B × D × A =** _____

3. A = 27   B = 9   C = 2   D = 6   E = 8   **(A × C) ÷ D =** _____

4. A = 4   B = 3   C = 2   D = 0   E = 1 $\frac{C}{A} - \frac{E}{C} =$ _____

5. A = 50   B = 99   C = 17   D = 3   E = 53   **B ÷ D + C =** _____

In each group, three words go together and two are the odd ones out. Underline the two words that do **not** go with the other three.

Example <u>define</u>   certain   sure   <u>give</u>   definite

6. satin   cashmere   jumper   silk   shirt

7. harmony   clamour   tranquillity   uproar   pandemonium

8. entrance   exit   bewitch   captivate   upstairs

9. mercury   earth   magnesium   aluminium   ground

10. reckless   benevolent   kind   spiteful   compassionate

Using the alphabet to help you, find the letter pair that completes each sentence. Write it on the line. You might need to use a different method from the example given.

A B C D E F G H I J K L M N O P Q R S T U V W X Y Z

Example **FG** is to **EF** as **LM** is to ___KL___.   (−1, −1)

11. **UG** is to **BK** as **SF** is to _____.

12. **RK** is to **LN** as **IX** is to _____.

13. **UO** is to **FL** as **HV** is to _____.

14. **TZ** is to **VT** as **DM** is to _____.

Work out the answers. Write your answers on the lines.

15. Zara did a survey about people's favourite sport. She found that 16% of people said swimming was their favourite sport and 46% of people said football. The remaining people said rugby was their favourite sport. What percentage of people said rugby was their favourite sport? _____

16. Tom works at a restaurant 6 days a week. On Monday and Tuesday he works 4 hours, and on Wednesday and Thursday he works 8 hours. The rest of the days he works 10-hour shifts. How many hours does he work in one week? _____

Score:		Time taken:		Target met?	

Target time: **10 minutes**

Underline the two words, **one** from each group, that best complete the sentence.

Example **Earth** is to (mud, dirty, <u>planet</u>) as **cow** is to (field, <u>mammal</u>, bull).

1. **Incomprehensible** is to (illegitimate, illegible, understandable) as **malfunctioning** is to (malicious, operational, especial).

2. **Page** is to (paper, book, consort) as **shelf** is to (bookcase, drawer, ornament).

3. **Allege** is to (clamber, hilltop, claim) as **forsake** is to (pray, abandon, accompany).

4. **Uniform** is to (standard, multiple, clothing) as **rancid** is to (rotten, sumptuous, appealing).

5. **Hundred** is to (millennium, century, ancient) as **ten** is to (decayed, decade, decide).

Find the missing number in each sequence and write it on the line.

Example 7   14   __21__   28   35   42   (+ 7 each time)

6. 70   61   52   43   _____   25   9. 57   56   58   57   _____   58

7. 4   8   16   32   _____   128   10. 7   27   47   67   _____   107

8. 36   9   36   _____   36   9

Find **one** missing letter that completes **both** pairs of words. Write it on the lines.

Example strea [_m_] ile   doo [_m_] arry

11. smel [__] ease   hal [__] rouble   13. appl [__] arn   salt [__] ank

12. vide [__] val   mang [__] nion   14. vira [__] ounge   spraw [__] apse

---

Work out the answers. Write your answers on the lines.

15. Joe is reading a book. The book has 600 pages and Joe starts reading on Monday. By Wednesday, he has read half the pages and on Thursday he reads 100 more. By Friday he has finished the book. His friend Charlie takes 6 more days to read the same book but Mustafa reads it in half Charlie's time. How many pages had Joe read by Thursday bedtime?
_____

16. Natalie loves to paint her nails. She has 20 different pots of nail polish. Half of them are shades of pink, 3 of them are blue, 4 are green and the rest are red. Her friend, Leila, brings round her collection of nail polish. She has half the number that Natalie has: 3 of her pots are shades of pink, half are green and the rest are silver or gold. How many pots of polish are **not** red or blue? _____

Score: _____   Time taken: _____   Target met? _____

Schofield & Sims

Target time: 10 minutes

Find the missing number in each of these equations and write it on the line.

Example $20 - 5 = 12 + $ ___3___

1. $(12^3 - 28) \div 2 = 400 \times 2 + $ _____
2. $10(7 \times 9) = 8^2 \times 10 - $ _____
3. $186 \div 6 = 310 \div $ _____
4. $\frac{1}{2} \times 300 = \frac{1}{3} \times $ _____
5. $1^2 + 1 = 100 - 68 - $ _____

Underline the pair of words that are most **opposite** in meaning.

Example (<u>lift, drop</u>)   (snow, wind)   (listen, learn)

6. (apparent, imaginary)   (accidental, intentional)   (injurious, judgmental)
7. (summon, dismiss)   (muster, collect)   (dividend, divide)
8. (silence, solitude)   (impoverish, poor)   (luxury, squalor)
9. (fantasy, reality)   (metaphor, simile)   (terror, horror)
10. (tyrant, dictator)   (incompetent, capable)   (interior, introvert)

Match the number codes to the words. One code is missing. Use this to help you work out the answers to the questions. Write your answers on the lines.

WISH   HIDE   DISH   WIDE   2169   6172   4172

What is the code for:

11. **HEED**? _____   12. **SWEDE**? _____   13. **HISSED**? _____
14. What does the code **79967** mean? _____

Circle the letter next to the **true** statement for each question.

15.   Carys plays the violin. The sound from a violin is produced by vibrating the strings with a bow.

If the above statements are true, which one of the following statements must also be true?
A   Carys plays the cello.
B   Carys plays in an orchestra.
C   Carys uses a bow to play her violin.
D   Violins are made from wood.

16.   Pasteurisation is a process of heating milk to a high temperature so that it can be preserved for longer. The process kills bacteria in the milk that could be harmful to people.

If the above statements are true, which one of the following statements must also be true?
A   Milk evaporates when it is pasteurised.
B   It is safer for humans to drink pasteurised milk than unpasteurised milk.
C   Pasteurised milk is more expensive than unpasteurised milk.
D   Bacteria can cause colds.

Score:	Time taken:	Target met?

Progress chart

Write the score (out of 16) for each test in the box provided on the right of the graph.
Then colour in the row next to the box to represent this score.

Section 1   **Total**

Test 1
Test 2
Test 3
Test 4
Test 5
Test 6
Test 7
Test 8
Test 9
Test 10
Test 11
Test 12

1 2 3 4 5 6 7 8 9 10 11 12 13 14 15 16
Score (out of 16)

Section 2   **Total**

Test 1
Test 2
Test 3
Test 4
Test 5
Test 6
Test 7
Test 8
Test 9
Test 10
Test 11
Test 12

1 2 3 4 5 6 7 8 9 10 11 12 13 14 15 16
Score (out of 16)

Section 3   **Total**

Test 1
Test 2
Test 3
Test 4
Test 5
Test 6
Test 7
Test 8
Test 9
Test 10
Test 11
Test 12

1 2 3 4 5 6 7 8 9 10 11 12 13 14 15 16

40   Score (out of 16)